*Love Is
a Baby*

Also by Joan Walsh Anglund

A Mother Goose Book

Christmas Is Love

A Friend Is Someone Who Likes You

The Brave Cowboy

Love Is a Special Way of Feeling

In a Pumpkin Shell

Christmas Is a Time of Giving

How Many Days Has Baby to Play?

Nibble Nibble Mousekin

Spring Is a New Beginning

Childhood Is a Time of Innocence

Morning Is a Little Child

Do You Love Someone?

A Cup of Sun

Love Is a Baby

Joan Walsh Anglund

GULLIVER BOOKS

HARCOURT BRACE JOVANOVICH, PUBLISHERS

SAN DIEGO   NEW YORK   LONDON

for Gideon Robert

Love is a baby . . .

so small and so new.

Love is bright eyes
that smile up at you.

Love is a rosy mouth,

wise without words,

And sounds as sweet
as the cooing of birds.

Love is a tiny hand
held in your own,
trusting and close,
so you're never alone.

Love is a cherub,

full of laughter and charm.

Love is an angel,
held safe in your arms.

A baby is the future,
beginning anew,

The start of a dream
just coming true.

A baby is the hope
of things yet to be . . .

Love is a baby!

Life's dearest gift to thee.

Library of Congress Cataloging-in-Publication Data
Anglund, Joan Walsh.
Love is a baby/by Joan Walsh Anglund.
p.   cm.
"Gulliver books."
Summary: Illustrated verse celebrates the joys of parenthood.
ISBN 0-15-200517-X
1. Infants — Juvenile poetry. 2. Children's poetry, American.
[1. Babies — Poetry. 2. American poetry.] I. Title.
PS3551.N47L68   1992
811'.54 — dc20   91-12248

Printed in Singapore

First edition
A B C D E